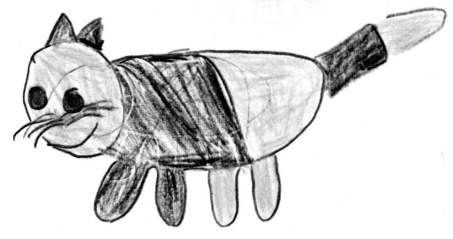

CATS
(and other crazy cuddlies)

Written by children
for pet lovers everywhere
Edited by
Richard & Helen Exley

UK: Exley Publications
Australia: Angus & Robertson Publishers

By the same editors:
The Missionary Myth (1973)
Grandmas and Grandpas (1975)
To Dad (1976)
To Mum (1976)
What is a Husband? (1977)
Happy Families (1977)
Dear World (1978)
Dogs (and other funny furries) (1978)

First published 1978. Copyright © Exley Publications Ltd, 63 Kingsfield
Road, Watford, Herts, United Kingdom, WD1 4PP.
Second printing August 1979
ISBN 0 905521 20 X (UK)

Published simultaneously in Australia by Angus & Robertson Publishers.
National Library of Australia Card number and ISBN 207 13749 8

Front cover drawing by Duncan Moxey, 13
Title page drawing by Kelly Davies, 8½
Back cover drawing by Guy Tucker, 7

Printed in Great Britain by Morrison & Gibb Ltd, Edinburgh.

My cat by Stuart Whittington, 4

Introduction

All the entries in *CATS and other crazy cuddlies* are the genuine work of children — and this is true of the illustrations as well as the words. Children were simply asked to describe life with their pets, and what their pets meant to them; this is the loving and sometimes hilarious result. Spelling has been left uncorrected to retain the freshness of the child's original entry.

Our thanks go to the many schools which helped, and to the thousands of children who sent in their entries for this and the companion book, *DOGS and other funny furries*. Almost all the entries were worth reading and we'd like to thank the children for helping to make our year's work such fun.

Richard & Helen Exley

What is a cat?

Cats have Babbys and cats Bang on the Back door and cats runaway form dogs and cats eat a lot of birds.

Simon Hurst, 8

A pet is the mysterious lump under the counterpane, the piteous mewing at half past seven in the morning, the prize mouse presented to you on your bedroom carpet, the muddy footprints on the clean washed floor.

Jemma de Vere Cole, 12

A pet is a living creature on which the family revolves. They walk it and feed it as though it did not have the brain to do it by itself. It is spoilt like an only child. It roams the streets at night and gets shoes thrown at it when it sings.

Stephen Dando, 13

A cat knows all the warm places, all the short cuts, and when its feeding time.

Gary Elliott, 12

Lana Sparks, 5

Yinka Bankole, 7

A well kept cat has fur as soft and as smooth as silk. Cats' eyes are pools of beauty and enchantment, and the way their oval pupils get smaller and bigger is just wonderful to watch.

Sheila Connell, 13

Cats know all the best places to sit. Cats like warm places like where someone else has been sitting.

Simon Kingham, 11

A pet means a scratching at the back door at ten o'clock at night, when you are comfortably tucked up in bed.

Debbie McNamara

Cats creep about very late
making ghostlike haunting wails.
They walk quietly wailing and purring
scaring the life out of people.

Agnes Wolfe, 11

Martin Cox, 8

Christopher Scott, 7

5

Just cats!

Sally Lake

Bella has had quite a lot of kittens, most of them we sell or give away, and the others go up to heaven.

Adam Case, 11

'You can let that cat in as long as it doesn't bother me' my father shouts. I open the door, the cat rushes through. Seconds later the cat rushes out my father chasing it. 'Get that cat out of my sight' he shouts.

David Simpson, 11

If you tickle his tummy he trys to bit but it is only a friendly bit.

Anna Gomall, 11

The pet I would most like to have would be a simese cat because they have long jumps and such beautiful fast movers. I like them also because they can be such messy anumals like myself sometimes.

Jeremy Nickalls,

we have a cat my sister uses him for Squeezing

Emily van Musschenbrock, 7

Susan Isherwood

My pet Bertie was a male until she had kittens.

Louise Allison, 10

Christopher Everall, 10

I know a cat that looks like a walking mop and it probably things that about me.

Elizabeth Cadogan, 11

The only thing that my dad doesn't like is when my cat leaves a mouse's kidneys splattered all over the crazy paving.

M Haberfeld, 11

I would like a kitten because I have no one to play with, because I have two brother's.

Katherine Menzies, 8

I had a cat that I used to cry on but she got killed and I cried even more.

Saffron Campbell-Jones, 10

Clare Pengelly, 12

7

Not that cat again

My cat is like a person of the faimley. Its norty of cores. But with out all are pets life word be a bore. Are cat is called Titten he is a big black fat Tom cat. He can be a nuisane by making muddy marks on the shelf and knock things of. Once he knocking a toy soder and it landed on Rurperts hea. Rurpert chuked it at Titten. The Titten pawnst on Rurpert. Rurpert skremed and chumped on me then the seat topled over and I was at the botem.

Timothy Gunstown, 7

Marion Baker, 10

If there is a hand, leg or body in the way he will attack it. I think it is very funny except when it's me.

J Lister, 12

When my cat sleeps in my bed he takes up more room than I do.

Peter Potts, 11

Schmutz is a cat of immense character. Schmutz can be stubborn, and very innocent looking. When I say he's annoying I mean he's annoying; you have a brand new pair of socks and he ladders them. He very rarely gets punished, but one of his favourite pastimes is bringing in juicy worms from the garden; and leaving them on the new carpet. I can remember him on one occasion placing a wriggling worm in front of the bathroom door, Mummy came out in bare feet and you can guess what happened. He was punished severely for that, but went straight out again and brought in another worm. Schmutz knows when he's been naughty, for his whiskers curl up and he disappears behind the settee.

Juliet Foster, 12

We got her a scratch pad but she likes the chair better.

Alastair Goodman, 9

Everybody thinks my cat is inocent but they are fooled.

Haroon Rahman, 10

9

One day Minnie knocked over her milk saucer it broke into two pieces. Then she went into the living room where she found a ball of wool and started rolling the wool around. When she had made a nice mess she climbed out of the tangle and onto the piano she let a music book fall to the ground. She sat down on the keys of the piano and fell asleep.

Amanda Sedley, 9

MILK

Nuisances

A cat is a nuisance, who chews your slippers, who bites your
fingers and worries your toes. A pet is a dustbin who eats all
your cheese, and pinches the cereal from the table top. A pet is a
pest who asks to go out, but changes its mind at the rain
outside, who opens all doors and leaps on all beds and knocks
off your ornaments and scratches the paint. What would we do
without a pet? We'd enjoy new slippers and paint without
scratches. We would not have to get up, out of a lovely warm
room to open a door to a soaking cat. But where would our
cushion go, our lovely warm ball, the rough little tongue and
the patter of paws?

Helen Salter, 14

I have a cat called Matilda. She frightened mummy beacause
She use to bit her toes. She is very big now and we give her cat
food but She ceep's caching mice all the time and she dose not
eat her food because She is not hungry the thing that we dont
like is she levese them at the back door soon we will have a pill
of dead mice at the door. She dose not bit our toes eney more
becaus I dont think she likes the tased.

Lucy Ellis, 8

Sometimes he sits on my homework or on a jigsaw puzzle just
to get attention if he feels left out.

Rebecca Plumb, 11

When I am doing my homework she pushes her nose in my
lap, and eventually I end up patting her and I have to do my
homework after she's fed up with being stroked.

Lisa Picton, 12

A perfect pet is a china cat, you don't have to take it out or
brush its hair or feed it, all it does is stand in a room, on a shalf.

Amanda Sim, 9

More nuisances

Our cats are without doubt the uniquest, lousiest, hungriest, fattest layabouts ever seen in Ormesby. When they are put out they do not catch mice as strays should, but lounge around at the front door, waiting for a chance to come in.

When they get bored with waiting they harmoniously commence a cats chorous with short solos from one or the other while the second gets its breath back. Occaisionally it gets as bad as the bagpipes and once in a while you get a long solo as the other cat goes round the back to give it to you in stereo.

But when the door is opened then follows a short interval for the cats to realize they havn't been fed. Then starts part two, which is only ever heard in mono as we havn't got two fridges.

Paul Merckoc, 12

Tat leaves his food wich is very rude. He is a norty cat but we love him so thats that.

Timothy Richard Furber, 6

Linda McConnachie

Screeching, Yowling that's what it's like to humans. To the cats it's like Handel, Bach or Schuman

Anne-Marie Hawkes, 11

Evil eyes

If you cross it suddenly the calm features of its face turn to evil and its soft paws spring sharp knives. Soon it comes back, the gentle intelegent cat, and you forgive it or rather it forgives you.

Gary Elliott, 12

When I sit in his favourite place he will have his vengeance by curling up on my lap and slowly digging his sharp claws into my legs.

Isabelle Parsons, 11

The cat is a loner, the tiger of the housing estate.

Joanne Lorimer, 13

Elspeth Marshall, 8

The hunter

He lies stretched out on the wall, a lazy striped tail dangling amongst the marigolds bobbing their heads in the pleasant summer sunshine. He rolls over onto his back and a powerfu˙ paw darts out now and again to pat the bees that hum busily in and out of the flowers and shrubs.

Suddenly he is on his feet, as a brown feathery object, floundering helplessly in the long grass attracts his attention. The beast slowly walks along the wall, his eyes never wavering from the little feathered ball. He crouches, his tail lying rigid and the whole of his body tense, remarkably still, frozen. He disappears behind a large bush, lost in its foliage. He appears, moments later, only a few yards from the innocent creature. He prepares for his spring. The huge muscles, power and craftiness, changing from a soft, cuddly cat to a ferocious, dangerous beast.

In a flash, he springs! The poor bird can only produce a fierce sqwark of defiance before it gasps its last breath. The cat, satisfied, returns to its favourite position on the wall, a long striped tail hangs limply amongst the marigolds.

Chez Liley, 12

There's two sides to a cat, one side is nice and fury, the other side is sharp.

Daniel Dass, 10

Marie James, 6

A sitting by the fire cat,
A homely friendly harmless cat.
A playful cat, an affectionate cat,
A curling round your feet cat.
A pink ball of wool is the victim of her play.

A tiger cat, a daring dashing tiger cat,
A bird flies past, she swings her tail.
A squeaky noise, she's on the ground,
Her wild eyes search the undergrowth.
A precise positioning of her paws,
And secretly silently one strong pounce,
Claws outstretched, a flutter of wings.
A high pitched scream, she's missed.

A sitting by the fire cat,
A playful cat, a tiger cat,
An original everyday tabby cat.

Rachel Cutler, 13

A slinking shape along the ground,
Not a rustle,
Not a sound,
Paws stepping carefully,
Around a tree,
What does he see?
A spring,
A sprawl of claw,
A dead bird lies upon the floor.

Jane Witheridge

Mouse is about looking for his lunch.
Cat is about waiting for his lunch.
Creeping silently across the mat.
Look out here comes cat.
Munch, crunch cat's had his lunch.

Claire Milburn, 10   *Lisa Wall, 9*

On the prowl

My pet wears small white socks. She's a crafty old thing is my little pet and she's fussy to match. She flicks her paw in and out of the fish bowl. She's frightened of getting her little white sock wet but I know she'd love to grab him.

Maureen Mcginley, 12

Sometimes my cat catches birds and he kills them and my mum smacks him but he is very pleased.

Kelly, 6

When we had some chicks we had to watch the cats. I looked out and saw that one had gone. Then Fudge came in holding a chick in his mouth fortunately Fudge has no teeth.

David Greene, 11

We saw feathers lying on the floor and there was of course no budgie in the cage. Alas! When the cat saw us we noticed a feather in his mouth so he ran out through the front door and my dad shouted don't come back and he didn't till two weeks later.

Peter Wright, 12

Claire Cummings, 9

About a year ago I won some goldfish at a fair, but guess who ate them?

Louise Allison, 10

Jean Harrison

Some cat characters

Pippin was Siamese and would only drink cream. We called her Pippin because my surname is Cox and there is a certain apple called 'Cox's Pippins', we all loved apples you see. One day Pippin left the garden which he only rarely did and later that day he came trotting home as pleased as punch carring an old, dirty, mucky piece of cucumber in his mouth. Why was he pleased? He was pleased for he had never caught a bird in his life and although the cucumber did not put up much of a fight he had a prize at last. He ate it on the garage roof and was sick.

Charlotte Cox, 11

Old fluffy cat grey and fat
Haughty and proud greedy and loud
If he can't have his way he'll howl all day.
When he eats up his food his manners are crude.
He's so disagreeable, his language is rude.
He thinks he's glorious he makes Mum furious!

Sharon Bosman, 13

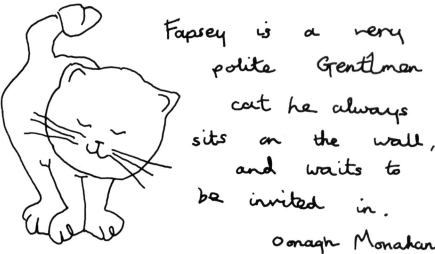

Fapsey is a very polite Gentlman cat he always sits on the wall, and waits to be invited in.

Oonagh Monahan

Tracey Wilcox

Oonagh Monahan

18

Most people believe that a cat takes but dosen't give. True it will rub against you and purr in a deep rumbling tone, but it does not care for you. It turns up for meals everytime it hears a can being rattled and demonstrates cupboard love.

But I have a cat with a difference. She has character, charm, cunning, and affection.

She has also selected her favourite television programme 'Match of the day'. She sits and tries to catch the ball. She repeats this dribbling a piece of screwed up paper round armchairs. I have taught her another trick where she actually retrieves the piece of paper. But she's the one who decides when its time to play and when its time to retrieve.

She will only eat her favourite food. If there is a food she dislikes she will raid the neighbour's bird table.

I have lived with her all her life and saw her being born, and everytime she comes in it is an irresistable temptation to pick her up, she is so lovable!

Steven Frame, 12

Marmalade's legs are patterned like pine-wood, and when he yawns he displays a magnificent cave, full of gleaming stalactites and stalagmites, fringed by a pink frill of rose-petal. At night he prowls along the walls, hissing and spitting, holding his tail as if it were starched. He stops every cat that dares to cross his path, like a high-way man.

Vicki Gould, 12

Ian Spellham, 12

Nine lives

Cats have nine lives so they say
well — last year on a fine summer's day
Smudge lost one!

It was wash day and our modern tub
Was giving our clothes a good scrub
Between wash, rinse and spin
Our cat Smudge clambered in
The crazy mischievous young cub.

We had just no idea
But something was queer —
As mum opened the door
Smudge fell out on the floor
One cat gone?

She was battered and wet
My poor little pet
A bit late for the vet

But wait, did she twitch
Then? and did one eye open?
Could there be hope yet?

We cuddled and hugged her,
Dried all her damp fur
And then heard a purr!

We were all in a tizzy
And Smudge was still dizzy
But by the next day
She was back at her play
Eight lives to go!

Yvonne Leater, 13

My dog has a girlfriend. She is a ginger cat but one day she got stuck in some cement. My dad got an 8lb sledge hammer to break her loose, but she never came again.

Kevin, 7

They say that cats have nine lives, but I reckon ours has ninety! He has fallen off the television aerial, onto the roof, and onto the water butt. The incident I remember best, however, is when he jumped into the freezer and stayed there for an hour! I think that if 'Tom and Jerry' are lucky, then our cat is miraculous!

Graham Monro, 12

Yvonne Leater

It's a dog's life being a cat

Dum dee dum, dee dum, dee dum, dee dum. Hallo! I have been thinking about telling somebody my life for a long time ... Its a dogs life being a cat. You have people screaming at you 'Look at that mess the cat's left, all white fur and hairs over my black skirt! kill it!' Charming. I can't help it if I'm not bald. Shes always blooming screaming at me!

I get harrasment. I only lie across the top of the TV because its warm. So what if my tail happens to flop across the screen, I'm sure its much nicer to look at than Hugie Green.

Oh! Oh! Here comes Mr Herliky, better move I'm sure he must take a size seven shoe, maybe nine. Ow! don't mind my poor paws then! Look here mate, if you want me to go out into the garden why don't you just ask me. Oh, ha ha! No, ha! don't lift me up ununun Ha! Ha! der der ararar Ha! ha no it tickles! No way can they understand my language only one thing they understand ... 'Arrgghhh!' He understood!

Bernadette Herliky, 13

They call me Pootchy-boos and Wiggy-wogga which I find quite undignified for a cat of my status. But they can be quite kind at times, and sometimes even go to the bother of putting out nice clean sheets on the things they call beds just so I can wipe my muddy paws.

Carl Mason, 11

Why can't I have the breast
Of the chicken, not the fat?
Why do I get the head
Of yesterdays sprat?

My life is good
My coat is a gleam
But do I have to have the milk
Why can't I have the cream?

Valerie Rice, 12

Clair Foster, 10

They call me soppy names and stroke me all day long. They use me as a blanket when their cold. They roll balls around the room expecting me to chase them.

Susan Hamill, 12

I share my house with a family of four. They are an odd lot really. They spend all their time washing up, cleaning cars, doing housework, prep and so on. I don't see they get anything out of life.

I have a great time, chasing mice, rushing round the garden and best of all sleeping in the best armchair.

However, humans do have their good points for I find it extremely hard opening a tin of cat food or a bottle of milk!

Edward Stansfield, 11

Tim Roberts, 10

Richard Tiffin,

His Lordship

When I decide to take a walk
I take it with dignity.
My velvet paws hardly touch the
Common pavement, and my tail curls
Most beautifully.
I am the greatest of them all.

Jemima Stratford, 9

When we are watching television Patch sits on the television
thinking we are watching him.

Richard Johnson, 10

You can teach a mynah to talk,
And teach a chimp to walk,
But you can't teach a cat anything
A cat knows it all.

Stephanie Lytton, 10

If she wants some food she will miaow non-stop. If she does
not like the look of it, she will flick her paw at the food, then
turn and look at us as if it was our fault. Then she flicks her tail
and walks out really stately. If you are sitting on her favourite
rug, she will try and push you off, she sits on you if that fails.

Josephine Healey

Everybody loves him, and he, perfectly amicably, loves nothing except himself.

Melissa Jones, 12

Lazy old mogs

Nickey is lazy, her occupation is sleeping all day.

Naseema Mohammed

When cats eat they make a noise and after they eat they go to sleep and their tummies go up and down and they purr.

Melanie Almark, 7

I have a cat
Who eats and sleeps and grows very fat.

Deirdre Hynes

The most extraordinary thing is that he never really even gets up.

Emma Whitworth

What a life he has!
No school.
No washing up.
No house work.
What a life!
Robert Hendy, 14

A perring delight
as the stars
shine brite
sleeping by the fire
a cat is corled up
Wot a perring delight.
Andrea Russell

Charlie asleep

Katy Aird, 9

26

A Day in the life of a cat

7.30   Came in

7.40   food

7.50   gone to livingroom.
7.51   washing on a chair.
8.15   Stopped washing, gone to sleep.

8.30   washing again.

8.50   sleep, same chair.

12.45   Opened one eye, stretched and sleep.

3.55   Got off chair
4.0   Looking for food, finished it.

4.10   Put out for run in garden

6.50   In for food.

6.60   sleep on chair.

S Ridgeway

Wholly mysterious

She stretches, languid, fluid, lank elegant paws extended.
She rises slowly, lean curves undulating.
She sits disdaining all.
In her green eyes glints of distant gleamings.
Hot steamy jungles.
Nights of fire or a sweet scented barge upon the Nile.
The ancient priests and incense burning.
Then she rubs against my legs.
And is a cat, our cat.
Plain 'Whisky', mouser of the first order.
Are they her dreams or mine?
Osiris and Ra and all the ancient learning.
What can our cat know of these?
But when her green eyes glow and the light
    shimmers on her black fur,
When she stands alone and untamed,
Then ancient wisdom, love of witches,
Seem to be but a shadow's distance.
A cat's leap into the unknown.

Shanta Sanyal

A cat is lovable with a complex mind that no mere mortal being can ever really understand.

Jackie Manning, 14

Lee Aspey, 10

She's as scaring as a witch, goblin and troll,
As swift as the wind and the running stream,
Lively like the playful fountains,
And as an enormous as the biggest mountains.

Her ears are so careful and gentle,
Her eyes are so creepy and oriental,
Her luminous eyes, show up more than light
Through the mysterious, lonely night.

Ambrose Treacy

Cats possess a beauty all of their own, a supple, silent strength.
Dogs are animals that make noisy demands and display their
affection, while cats are content to live alongside their owners,
remaining remote, independant and wholly mysterious. The
unemotional stare of a cat gives away nothing of its feelings.

Simon Milligan, 12

Some odd habits

If it happened to be a cold night Sammy, my cat, would end up coming under the bed covers with me of his own accord (well sometimes).

Karen Nelder

Tupence's hobbies are trying to catch birds and tearing apart pom-poms.

Suzanne London, 12

Sometimes she casually sticks out a paw to wash and then she forgets completly what she was going to do with it. So she waits a few minutes and then puts it back down again.

Lucy Miranda Ward, 8

Appollo's exercise is a very rapid steeple chase round the house ending with a dance along the key board of our piano.

Roger Mann, 12

This Smorning my Cat got On the hand basin and Looked under the tap.
cristiano Macis

AAAAAA

My cats silly,
When he hits his head on the arm of the chair,
He sits on the floor for a few minutes,
And then he jumps up at the chair,
And hits it even harder.

Joanne Compton, 10

My cat Daisy is always munching away
at food just like Jenny my sister.

John Dick, 7

Angela Benton, 10

Mut keeps brining in worms and putting in my mum's
slippers or on the floor where they can't be seen. She takes a fur
toy mouse around the house with her. She speaks to it as well.

A Cotton, 10

I have taught my cat a trick, I bring my ball and machine-gun.
She balances on the ball and I fire my machine-gun and she
falls off and pretends that she is dead.

Kevin Kelly, 8

Big sister calls it the little kitten with the big fat tum which
isn't suprising because it eats anything it sees like leaves, paper
and cat food. We can't see what's on television because it eats
the Radio and TV times.

Christopher Shilwock

My favourite cat sleeps
in my bed and he won't
eat caramel wafers unless
the fire is on.

David Ashton, 7

Sir Thomas Tuck and others

My cat is called Tom. He has been knighted by the man who lives upstairs. So he is Sir Thomas Tuck now.

Sara Tuck, 10

We call him Kitty, I don't know why because he is now fully grown; but I somehow feel he will always be Kitty. He's got hundreds of other names. These include Cameron, Roary, Pussy, Your Highness, The Emperor of the French, and Napoleon. My Father when he gets cross with him calls him Cat.

Sheena Anderson, 11

I have a pet and it is a cat and it is a he his name is Parkinson and Parky for short and when is on tv we shout him to come and see himself but he dose not come.

Suzannah Skinner, 7

My cats name is Lester Piggot,
He runs faster than a Horse.

Jason Staples, 9

We have a cat
Called Puddy Tat

Paul Carter, 9

Steven Edwards, 5

My cat moves so silently i cannot hear him and his name is James Bond.

Jason Phillips, 7

◁ *Trevor Butterworth, 7*

Cuddlies

I think my kitten is so beautiful and I love him very much, I hope he thinks the same about me.

Alison Maher, 13

My cat called thomas tickles me with his soft fur he tickles me with his whiskers and makes me laugh I love him

Sean, 7

I love my cat called Thomas, because he is all fluffy and cuddly and in the morning he comes up to my bed and purrs in my ear to wake me up.

Rachel Gill, 9

A pet is a little snug ball in a basket.

Shashi Bala, 10

I love my pet very dearly
As if it was part of my family
When its asleep I look at its
   soft white snowy coat
It looks like a small ball of fur
To stroke so tenderly and dearly
A friend you can turn to lovingly

Anthea Charlton, 11

Richard Joinson

That cats so lovly
Im glad its mine

o yes o yes

I m glad its mine.

Alison McAlpine, 11

◁ *Catherine Drake, 8*

Loving each other

I like patch because he does not like to be alone.

Richard Johnson, 10

Tabby I think is the best cat in the world because when you cry she come up to you and kisses you better so too if you are shouting loud.

Frances Morton

Cats are intelligent animals, they understand you in their own way. If you say something they will look up at you and you think they know what you say.

Stephen Dunford, 13

My pet is a cat and will see you do things but will never tell anybody, it will just give you that kind of look as if to say, I won't tell — don't worry.

Karen Evans, 14

When your mom and dad, sister and brother have gon out your cat is alway by you.

Errol Grant, 10

a cat is soft and furry and loves you

Rebecca Ferrol, 5

I sat back down and shut my eyes and reviewed over the day
then Snowy made a running leap for my lap I don't mind her
getting on but if my dad finds cat hairs on my trousers he
might hit me but that worry did not cross my mind when she
settled down I felt relaxed and all of the tensions of the day
floated away as Snowy my jet black cat lay on my lap purring.

Sharon Harris, 14

Twelve o'clock comes, the curtains are drawn
The little cat comes, whats going on?
He heads for the kitchen, gets milk from the bowl
Then curls up beside me and keeps my toes warm

Anne-Marie McGuigan, 9

Sherrie Ridley, 10

She ought to have known

The old woman heaved herself out of the chair and went to put the kettle on. She tightened the shawl around her shoulders, it was very cold in her little flat, she couldn't afford to keep the fire on very long, an hour or two at the most. She looked around, who would have thought that she would sink to this? A two roomed flat at the back of a decrepit house in the East End of London. But she supposed that she was lucky, that Mrs Thomkin down the road had been moved into an Old People's Home and she wouldn't like that. No, whatever the flat was, it was home, it might have rising damp, mildew and rats ... drat those pesky rats, there was one now scratching and scuffling. But wait those sounds came from outside the door, a pitiful miaouw, it was just another stray cat. The kettle started whistling, she poured her tea out and put a drop of milk in it. That was another thing, the price of milk these days, she remembered the time when it was fourpence a gallon, as it was now she got two pints a week and lucky at that. There went that cat again, she opened the door. 'Shoo Pussy! Shoo!' The cat slunk in past her. Disconcerted the old woman shut the door, she had some right nosy neighbours. 'Shoo Pussy' she tried again. The cat lay on her rug purring, the flat was cold but not as cold as outside. The old woman softened; she had had a cat like that when she was a girl. She poured some milk onto a saucer, there went her breakfast tea. Poor cat, didn't look as if he'd had a decent meal for weeks; the old woman went to the larder door, she had that nice piece of fish she'd been saving for dinner, still the cat looked awfully hungry. When he had finished his meal, he stretched luxuriously and leapt onto the old woman's lap. She reached for the paper and her glasses, her eyes had been getting very bad lately. She moved slightly, the car purred, she'd forgotten he was there. He felt warm and safe, so did the old woman, she hadn't felt so warm for a long time, the fire wasn't on either. The cat jumped

down and padded softly to the door.
'Not going already pussy?' asked the old woman suddenly turning cold. The cat just looked at her. Slowly she opened the door. 'Go on then, don't let me stop you', she said bitterly. The cat walked out.

That night the old woman cried herself to sleep. She was alone again. In the morning she woke just in time to hear the milkman leaving, that meant she wouldn't talk to another person all day unless her neighbour called. It was too cold to go shopping and besides she had no money.

A scratching sounded on the door, the old woman smiled, she ought to have known he wouldn't forget. She opened the door, 'Come in Pussy', she said.

Judith O'Reilly

Edward Pelling, 7

Other crazy cuddlies

We had some hamters my mummy told me not to put them together. One night I put them together in a cage. They had babys, 16 of them.

Simon Wood, 10

My sister had a hamster called Zip. We mated it with a friend's hamster called blogs. Zip and blogs had eight babies. I liked Zip so much that I might get another one. I will probble get one from Edwinas hamster called Candy. Candy is Zips childs child, which means I will get one of Zips childs childs child.

Trinity Fry, 9

My hamster never bites people especially girls.

Victoria Hilditch, 6

I love little Pegusus.
He is so warm and sweet.
And he squeaks to say "Thank you"
Cause he's not rude:

Mark Johnson, 9

Neil Simpson

Sernjeet Sandhu, 7

Steven Blackmore, 6

I had pet canary. His name was Fred and when we bought him we thought he was a boy. But one day he laid eggs so Fred wasn't really a Fred after all.

Scott Burgess, 11

They amuse you by chasing after there tail or by rolling a bale with its nose. When you are sad a pet feels that you are upset about something and tries to comfort you.
When they have done something wrong you always know because they cannot keep an inocent face. Some sit in the corner and others roll over to be tickled.

Julie, 9

My daddy is a vet. The more pets people get the more pocket money I get.

Simon Furber, 8

I think that pets finish the family off because you can't play with a brush or a bath.

Richard Langrish, 7

Whats this a rabbit

dan't be

stupid

its a cat

Deana McNicol

What is a pet ?

A pet is muddy foot-prints on the kitchen floor.

Sarah Hoskin, 13

A pet is a round, barrel-shaped object with sleek fur, piggy eyes, a boot-button nose, four shabby legs and a waggy tail.

Sarah Hoskin, 13

A pet is a little face that waits at the window.

Angela Gentles, 10

Without a pet, a family wouldn't be complete.

Katie Edgington, 11

A pet is what is big and what is small.

Joanna Rose, 10

Pets do everyone a world of good.

Nicola White, 14

Dorothy Tait, 13

Sally Watton

42

Pets are more like humans than humans are.

Fiona McCallig

With out a pet the house would be so lonely and ever so calm.

Timothy Klemz, 10

A pet is for messing up your sewing box.

Elizabeth Evered, 11

A pet is something that people pour out all their troubles onto. When with a pet people often behave like babies.

Serena Jones, 12

I love my pet because it does not tell you off for being naughty.

Lynne Lewis, 13

Pets can run, skip, fly, jump or crawl down the back of your neck.

Sharon Kemble, 12

A pet is an animal which has been taken into care by a family.
Claire Kelly, 9

Wahida Jafferji

Amanda Crouch, 10

M Holden, 8

44

Limericks and crazy rhymes

I had a little hamster, I kept it in a cage
One day my little nephew killed it in a rage
It's gone away to heaven now, or so that's what they say
But I know that really, the dustbin men took him away
Sarah Williams, 11

I wish my cat had boots to wear,
For when the day is wet
He never stops to wipe his feet,
A fact I do regret.
Shirley Evans, 13

There was a coo
In yonder fild
its ney there noo
it musta shifted
David Potter, 9

Cat is a sly cat
He has this habit
of behaving like a rabbit
on Sundays and on Mondays.
Lucy, 8

There once was a gnu from Peru,
Who found it had nothing to do.
So it sat on the stairs,
and counted its hairs,
And found it had seventy-two.

Mandy Neilson, 15

Beware of the human

My budgie sat down by the hoover with his head on his side, and then all the sudden the hoover sucked him in. Now thinking back on it, it was rather funny seeing him covered in dust, but at the time it was disatorus. I took the hoover apart and found the budgie in the middle of the dust back. He flew around the room a couple of times. By now there was dust everywhere, and I had to clean all over again, but I wasn't angry because I was so glad that the budgie was alive safe and well.

Glesni Jenkins

When I had goldfish my brother used to stick his head in the tank and try and eat it so we gave it away.

Amanda Sharp, 9

Kate Oddie, 11

I had some fish, I had six
and they kept fighting until
there was only one left
and I boiled it by accident

by Malcolm Dyer

I used to have a rabbit called Whiskers. My next door
neighbour his aways making fun of him and saying he could
do with using him for a rabbit pie. There hapened to be a small
hole in the bottom of the fence and one day it got through the
fence and ate all his best cabbages. Well the neighbour was
furious he nearly wrung his knek. The next day he boreded up
the hole in the fence and put a picture of a rabbit pie on the
wood.

Tracy Townley

Buster lets you play with him, he will let you do nearly
everything with him, He lets you wear him round your neck
like a scarf.

David Levin

I used to have a white rabbit but he had babies and he died.
Daddy wanted to cook him but I wouldn't let him but he put
him in a stew just the same.

Judith Bowen, 7

Ko Jack and Delila

I have eight birds and one was born with no feathers on his head so we could him Ko Jack.

Matthew Rowe, 8

I do wish I had a fluffy white rabbit. I would call him Starsky because he would have a hutch.

Rosemary Sutton, 7

UFO was a fluffy brown gerbil.
Scuttling fast on four delicate feet,
At night, when all was quiet,
Two twinkling eyes would appear.

Tessa Duggleby, 12

I have two Pet mice one is called Thinnifer because it is thin and the other one is called Fattpuff because it is fat.

Carie Hodes, 8

When we got home we tipped the goldfish into some clear water and then my mum suddenly saw that he only had one eye. My mum started hunting for his other eye in the muddy water but she couldn't find it and I was glad because I didn't know what we would have done if we had found it. So that is why we call him Nelson.

Karen Martin, 11

When we got back the fat fish was at the bottom of the bowl with a part of his body eaten. I do not put my finger in the bowl and I named him Jaws.

Simon Ferguson, 7

I called my hamster Hammy; no marks for originality but I found there was no proper name that would capture what I felt about him.

Joanna Scott, 12

I had a hamster named Bungo who I thought smelt quite alright but Dad thought differently, so he called it Pongo.

Ian Knox, 11

My guinea pig is called Humpty because he is always falling out of his cage.

Richard Beniston, 11

I have a hamster called Tarzan. I called him Tarzan because he used to climb up the bars on his cage and let go of one paw.

Elizabeth Stokes, 9

I would like an alligator. I would call it Toothache.

Mitchell Clark, 9

Delila.

key.
white.

Julie Scaturro

Mums being driven quietly potty

I had a pet lizard called Albert,
Now one night he was very naughty
He got loose and we couldn't find him
Until mummy got into bed,
And then you can guess what happened.
She jumped out of bed with a scream.
That was the end of poor Albert.
Nothing could make mummy change her mind.

Jasmine Pinto, 12

My dad said I've got a surprise. My brother and I said What is
it. Then he said, its a mouse. My Mum screemed and jumped
on a chair. Then my Dad said, you don't have to worry its only
a baby. It was a life of comotion for my Mum. Every time the
mouse got loose my Mum started screeming and jumping on
chairs. Soon, so many chairs had been jumped on they
callasped.

Jaspal Saund, 9

A pet may be anything,
Provided mum lets
it in the house.

Jane Wise, 13

50

Andrew Gray, 10

The mice twins were a funny little pair, one was called Stripe and the other Tom Thumb.
I let them lose in my bedroom and could not find them. So I went to bed very sad. In the middle of the night I was woken up. I found Tom Thumb and Stripe had bitten a hole in my pyjamas and the mattress. This was a funny site but mummy was not very pleased because she had to buy me a new mattress because they had made a nest in it. I was pleased I had them back.

Susannah Elizabeth Knight, 11

A pet is like your brother,
A pet is to annoy your mother.

Jill Stephenson, 11

One day whilst I was watching tv, I saw these beautiful little lion cubs, it was then I made my mind up I would choose a lion. I told mum about my desicion, but somehow she didn't seem to like the idea.

Glen W Jones, 14

Pets are things that people keep,
Some have cows and some sheep,
Some have birds and some have bats,
My mum settled for four little brats.

Peter Devlin, 12

51

Sarah Sim, 6

My fish dus do nothing

Christopher Rowand

Round and round and round

I am glad I dont live in a fish tank but they dont seem to mind.

Tami Hoad, 6

I do not like Splish and Splash because they are always wet. All they do is sit there in the goldfish bowl and guzzle.

Simon Kirkup, 11

A goldfish just swims round and round and round and round and round and round and round and round and is very boring.

Sharon Kemble, 12

My pets now are fish. They are pretty and quiet. But I don't like them much; they are so cold. I used to have two dogs when I was younger. Zazy was a collie, and Kushy was a wolf-dog. They both got killed and I cried a lot. Now my father has decided to have fish so that I won't love them and be sad when they die.

Hagit Torga, 14

No I wouldn't have a fish because it can't come for a walk.

Anthony Riddle, 10

I had a little goldfish
It swam around all day
It swam around in circles
And drove me round the bend.
Evette McDonald, 9

Cats go mieou
Dogs go woof,
Mice go eek
Fish go glug.
Aileen Duncan, 9

David Vineall, 10

Worms and other wierdies

I would like a snake an adder because it would bite all the girles and all the buoys cold play with it.

Nigel Matthew, 8

Worms are not the slimy creatures they are made out to be. When I think of a worm, I think of a pretty little thing. Even though I like worms, sometimes I drop them out of shock.

Jennifer Brown

The worm slithers in the wormery
I pick it up,
It squirms in my hand,
Then tries to escape down my sleeve
A cold damp feeling shivers down my spine
So I put him back in the wormery.
A worm might not seem much of a pet to you
But it means a lot to me.

Roger Tancock, 12

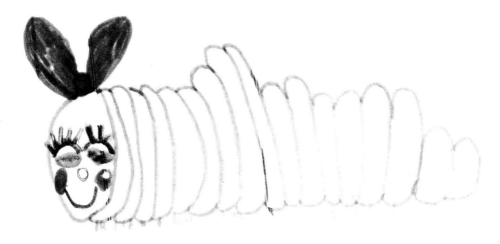

Jennifer Brown

If I had an octopus, I could let it do all my chores, all at once.

Patricia Johnston

I wish I could have a lion because if I went to a football match if any people pick on me I could get my lion on them.

David May, 11

I have always wished since I was a little girl to own a huge tiger. To have it all to myself from an early age onwards, all cuddly and playful.

When they are small they look so fragile and lost, that you can't help feeling you want one. And when they grow up it's different they're even more lost looking, as if trying to ask us to take them and help them.

I just can't help wishing I had one all to myself just to cuddle all the time. It is such a pity we're not allowed to keep one.

Karen Lewis

Sultan is my 'pet'; unusual possibly, but nicer (to me) than cat, dog or canary. He is a Blackbird. Of the group I feed, and whose behaviour I record, Sultan is the most amiable, and fattest. He is five years old, and is getting stout and grey. He can't resist a fight and has beaten a cat in a straight fight. I named him Sultan because he is the dominant male and because of his fondness for dried fruit, (especially sultanas). He is also known as fatbird and Billy Bunter.

Blackbirds aren't the only birds we feed. We also have a sparrow who thinks he's a blackbird, a thrush who thinks he's a human, a robin who thinks he's a thrush, and an assortment of sparrows, starlings, a crow, greenfinches, bullfinches, blue, coal and great tits who think of nothing except eating.

Timothy B Jones, 12

More wierdies

If I had a fawn I would ride to school on him. I would not have to pay for bus fares I could go by fawn.

Felicity Blakeley, 10

I would like to have a giraffe. I could climb up my giraffe and I would be able to see evrything and then I could slide down my giraffe. All my bad friends get kiked by my giraffe. I will call him Hector.

Giles Martin, 8

If I was given three wishes, I would ask for a small fortune, a sports car and a tame tiger. The last choice may seem a little unusual, but a little individualism has never harmed anyone.

Michelle de Cordova, 12

I would like a tiger. My mum wouldn't like a tiger because it would be too big. It would be hard to take to the Supermarket. It would go after everyone and people would bump into tins. I wouldn't be able to go to Trafalgar because he would eat all the pigeons. In the park we could play ball and teach him to skip. I love tigers.

Julie Larkin, 11

I would like a hippopotamus. I would have a big muddy pool at the end of the garden. The problem would to keep it out of the house. I could teach it to skateboard. Taking it down to the shops could be the biggest problem. I'd put a paper bag over my head.

Alan Walsh, 11

I was on my way through the jungle. Suddenly a blue panther pounced out from some bushes and dug its claws into a nearby tree. I jumped back in surprise and groaned unhappily and said, 'Poor chap he just won't do. He's not pink.'

Andrew Thomas, 12

My mom would like a crocodile to eat up all the leftovers and when I didn't like a friend I would drop him in.

Gavin Hurd, 7

About cruelty and captivity

Because the world is completely ruled by humans, species are being wiped out, animals are being killed or put in cages for all to gawp at, or to be trained to make money for the species that captured them.

Samantha Parsons, 14

The cat family is the finest in the world, and the greatest of the cats is the tiger. It is sad, is it not, that weak, feeble little humans are destroying him — bit by bit?

Michelle de Cardova, 12

Animals which are killed and sold as coats, have been murdered for someone to go strutting round in a more expensive coat than 'the Jones'.

Samantha Parsons, 14

Animals are to be treated with respect. We must inflict as little discomfort as possible on them if we are to call ourselves humans with superiority over creatures which have weaker intelligence but just as strong a sense of pain as us.

Catherine Wood, 15

Animals are treated very badly. They are killed for sport, for cosmetics, dog food, for us to eat, for their skins and for experiments. When they were using them for testing smoking it was very very mean on the dogs. Why should they suffer for the faults we make?

Julie Nolan, 12

People put mice traps to try and trap them
But I think It is craul to do that
Becouse mice are only little.

Carol Ramsden

Another abuse of animals is keeping them in cages for most of the time, moving them around the country, and letting them out to do unnatural tricks to make people laugh. What is the thrill in denying an animal its dignity? They are much more interesting when they are behaving normally.

Catherine Wood, 15

There are over five hundred dogs in the nearest RSPCA kennels to you. And if they are not claimed within two weeks they are destroyed. I think dogs that have been thrown out should be rescued, cleaned up and given to people who really will look after them. There are certainly enough pets in this country, so I think they should stop selling any more until the ones that are already there have good homes and are well looked after.

Zoe Robinson

Don't trap animals

Roddy Galbraith   age 7

My friend has a Hamster
he is very bad. He has been
found in the loo. He has bitten
though the telephope wire. If he
has the chance he will jump
from a bunk bed.

Paul Emerson, 8

Silly Billies

A rabbit you may think is a lovable animal well mainly they are but not mine. Mine is a member of the IRA because he can never stop fighting. He rides a skateboard, chews up Tennis balls and jumps on top of the tortoise.

Jeffrey Revell, 11

My hamster, Joshua was the smallest of the flock of those daft things that come from a place called a pet shop. One day I said 'Hello Joshie,' he fell 'Splat!' into his milk. I lifted him from his cage and gave him a warm shower, it served him right and I told him so, but he bit me.

Claire Taylor, 10

I once had three goldfish. They were great television addicts. Their favourite programme was the circus and the acrobats. So my heroic goldfish tried to copy them. One day my fish attempted the daring and difficult double flip. I do not have any goldfish any more.

Alison Campbell, 14

One night when I was in bed the little fish and the big fish were going mad and suddenly the big fish went mader than ever and the little fish blew bubbles and jumped right out of the fish bowl and he went back in again and my mum turned round and laughed and when my daddy came home my mummy told him about the little fish going out of the bowl and coming back in the bowl again and my daddy laughed and my mummy laughed too and then in the morning my mum told Clive and he laughed but when my mummy told me I didn't laugh like dad and Clive did.

Louise Anstey, 8

Never lonely

A pet is a friend when you have no one.

Paul Everett, 14

Pets can bring happiness to many families and make old people feel less lonely. Just the presence of a cat or a dog can alter the atmosphere of a room and make it less quiet and lonely.

Mary Gregory, 13

A pet is someone to welcome lonely and old people home, becuase it is horrible to always come home to an empty house. A pet depends on its owner for food, warmth and love, and this makes a lonely person feel they are needed.

Angela Bracken, 10

Marlene Parada

A pet to me is a friend when you need someone to talk to. Although it can't understand it will hold out a paw.

I love my pet because it plays with me when all my other friends have gone home.

Daniel Dass, 10

Pets are like an only friend to some old people. Cats curl up upon their laps and keep them warm. Dogs guard them when they are in Danger. Some pets make the old feel a young and adventurous person again. Pets seem to remain forever remembered to them. Pets seem to live inside the old. Pets are good and warm hearted and treat the old well. Pets know when the old are troubled, and try to keep up their spirits by being pleasant. But most of all, I think that a pet is valued to them because they seem to understand.

Tracey Whittock, 12

We all know pets can't talk but mine talks all the time, says he's sorry, thanks you, and sympathises when no one else will.

Suzanne Ramsay, 10

A pet is a friend you can turn to when others go against you. A pet is a protector.

Sharon Graham, 11

What are pets
pets are animls
Thet you luv.

Lucy, 6

Some other interesting EXLEY titles now available

See Britain at Work, £4.95
This guidebook details hundreds of glassworks, craft workshops, potteries, factories etc. open to the public and to schools. An invaluable family reference book.

Shopping by Post, £5.50
Hundreds of firms which will supply goods by post. 'An excellent book' (Marge Proops).'Extraordinarily comprehensive' (Sheila Black). Invaluable for those who live far from good shops.

The Magic of London's Museums, £4.95
This illustrated guide to all London's museums — almost 100 of them — will provide endless ideas for a rainy day. Ideal for teachers, parents and holidaymakers.

Dear World, £6.95
'How I would put the world right, by children of 50 nations'. An unusual and beautifully illustrated book, in colour.

What is a husband? £2.50
7,500 real wives answered that question and the best quotes are here. Pithy, beautiful, rude, hilarious, sad, romantic. Buy a copy for your anniversary!

Old is great: £2.50
A book that pokes fun at youth and revels in the first grey hairs of middle age. 'An irreverent sometimes bawdy, loo-side book for anyone over 30. Furiously funny', says the Good Book Guide.

Grandmas & Grandpas, £2.50
'A Grandma is old on the outside and young on the inside.' This charming little book with all the entries written by grandchildren solves many a present problem.

To Dad, £2.50
'Fathers are always right, and even if they're not right, they're never actually wrong.' Dads will love this book. Also in the series: *To Mum, Happy Families, CATS (and other crazy cuddlies), DOGS (and other funny furries).*

All these books are obtainable through your local bookshop, or by post from Exley Publications, 63 Kingsfield Road, Watford, Herts, WD1 4PP. Please add 10p in the £ as a contribution to postage.